SAN FRANCISCO BOTANICAL GARDEN
at Strybing Arboretum

An Introduction to a World of Plants

PETER DALLMAN *and*
SCOT MEDBURY

Published by the
SAN FRANCISCO BOTANICAL GARDEN SOCIETY

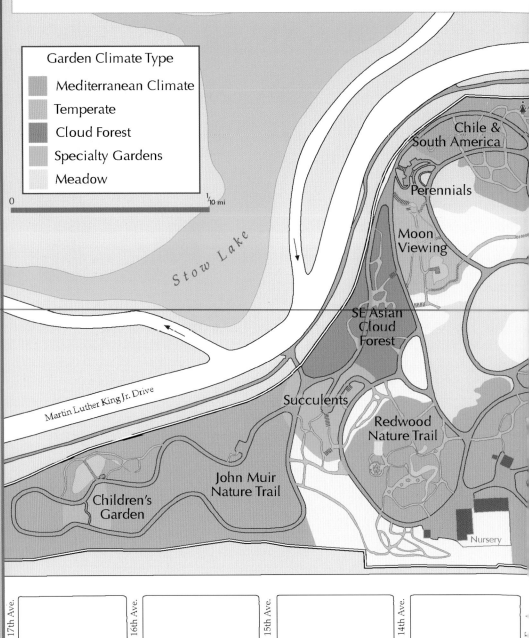

SAN FRANCISCO BOTANICA

Golden

Garden Climate Type

- Mediterranean Climate
- Temperate
- Cloud Forest
- Specialty Gardens
- Meadow

0   1/10 mi

Stow Lake

Chile & South America

Perennials

Moon Viewing

SE Asian Cloud Forest

Martin Luther King Jr. Drive

Succulents

Redwood Nature Trail

John Muir Nature Trail

Children's Garden

Nursery

17th Ave.

16th Ave.

15th Ave.

14th Ave.

GARDEN at Strybing Arboretum

ate Park

Japanese
Tea Garden

DeYoung Museum

California
Academy
of Sciences

North

Friend Gate

ustralia

Primitive
Plants

Rhododendrons

Fragrance

Wildfowl
Pond

after-hours
exit

To
Conservatory
of Flowers,
.5 mi

New
Zealand

Fountain

South Africa

Demonstration
Garden

Great Meadow

Book
store

Entry

**Main
Gate**

Meso-American
Cloud Forest

Library

after-hours
exit

Gallery

Big Rec
Ball Field

California

Meeting
Rooms

East Asia

Offices

71

Lincoln Way

12th Ave.

11th Ave.

10th Ave.

44

9th Ave.

44

N

Judah

One block to
Muni Metro

Produced for and available from:

    San Francisco Botanical Garden Society
    Golden Gate Park
    9th Avenue at Lincoln Way
    San Francisco, CA 94122

First Edition
ISBN 0-9607890-5-7
Phyllis M. Faber
Pickleweed Press
Mill Valley, CA 94941

Printed in Hong Kong through Global Interprint, Santa Rosa, CA

Cover and book design and typesetting by Beth Hansen-Winter
Cover photographs by Saxon Holt

CONTENTS

ACKNOWLEDGMENTS

Phyllis Faber produced and edited this book, helping us achieve a reader-friendly style and organization of topics. She made numerous insightful suggestions and comments. Her long experience publishing books about California's plant life was a great asset in the production of this book.

We were also lucky to have had Beth Hansen-Winter as designer. Her creativity and love of plants are evident in her selection of photographs and in the layout of the book.

Barbara Pitschel, head librarian, and Kathleen Fisher, associate librarian at the Helen Crocker Russell Library, provided their generous help in a welcoming and pleasant setting.

We are grateful for the beautiful maps that were created by Darin Jensen, staff cartographer, University of California, with the help of summer cartography interns Chad Johnson, Thomas Leroe-Munoz, Daniel McChesney-Young, Marcy Protteau, and Jesusa Romero.

Photographs were generously donated by Saxon Holt and Joanne Taylor and are identified with their names. Many thanks! All other color photographs are by Peter Dallman.

We received helpful suggestions from docents Marian Feigenbaum, Katherine McNeil, Joanne Taylor, Darin Dawson, and Joseph Barbaccia of the San Francisco Botanical Garden Society. Don Mahoney, horticultural manager, and both Bian Tan and Tony Morosco, former and current plant collections managers, provided valuable assistance.

Peter's wife Mary, son Tom, and friend Vincent Scardina helped with many aspects of this book and earned his deep gratitude. The support and encouragement of Scot's life-partner Brian Lym and of the Botanical Garden's inspiring staff, especially Susan Nervo, are also gratefully acknowledged.

WELCOME TO THE GARDEN

We invite you to experience the beauty and richness of the **San Francisco Botanical Garden at Strybing Arboretum**, located in Golden Gate Park and open every day of the year.

This guide offers the visitor three walks, each exploring a different part of the Garden.

- **The Turn** makes a loop between the two entrance gates. It begins with views of the Great Meadow and central fountain and then visits the Demonstration, Fragrance, Rhododendron, Primitive Plant, and South Africa gardens.

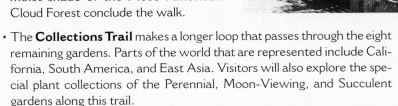

- The **Garden Walk** covers the central area of the Garden between the Friend Gate and the western side of the Great Meadow. It introduces plants from Australia and New Zealand and revisits the South Africa garden, all representing plants of the Southern Hemisphere. Colorful tropical forest plants in the deep moist shade of the Meso-American Cloud Forest conclude the walk.

- The **Collections Trail** makes a longer loop that passes through the eight remaining gardens. Parts of the world that are represented include California, South America, and East Asia. Visitors will also explore the special plant collections of the Perennial, Moon-Viewing, and Succulent gardens along this trail.

The Garden spreads over 55 acres that lie only 2.5 miles from the Pacific Ocean, near the northern tip of the San Francisco peninsula at the Golden Gate. In this location, an ocean-moderated climate favors the growth of an enormous variety of plants. The Garden grows over 7,500 plant species from around the world. The plants are grouped by their countries of origin and in settings that recall their native landscapes.

The Garden is owned and operated by the San Francisco Recreation and Park

OPPOSITE: **Children on the Great Meadow;** ABOVE: **Japanese maple** (*Acer palmatum* 'Ever Red') **in the Library Courtyard.**

Department of San Francisco in cooperation with the San Francisco Botanical Garden Society, a non-profit, member-supported organization which raises funds to support the Garden. The Society offers educational programs and supports the Helen Crocker Russell Library of Horticulture. The Library, located near the Main Gate, welcomes visitors to enjoy Northern California's most comprehensive collection of horticultural books and journals.

A SPECIAL PLACE

The Garden specializes in growing plants that are native to three different climates found in select places around the world:

- A **mediterranean climate** characterized by warm dry summers and mild wet winters. This climate is similar to our own and is found only in five locations around the world, namely in parts of California, Chile, South Africa, Australia, and the lands around the Mediterranean Sea.

- A mild **temperate climate** with year-round rainfall found in parts of East Asia, Australia, New Zealand, and South America. These conditions are maintained in our gardens by watering during the dry summer.

- A moist **tropical cloud forest climate** typical of high mountain slopes that are kept cool by cloud cover and drizzle. Our summer fog and moist mild winters mimic these conditions. The Garden is unique among botanical gardens in being able to maintain a rich outdoor collection of cloud forest plants.

TOP TO BOTTOM: Fuchsia-flowered gooseberry (*Ribes speciosum*); Paperbush MITSUMATA (*Edgeworthia chrysantha*); *Senecio petasites*.

AN IDEAL LOCATION

San Francisco's famous fog further moderates an already mild mediterranean climate. The fog is kind to plants, bringing moisture and moderate temperatures during the dry summer half of the year. The average year-round temperature in San Francisco is 57° F, with a seasonal difference between summer and winter of only 10°. Summer days typically remain under 80° and only a few winter nights are colder than 40°. Given these conditions, the plant collections feature many frost- and heat-intolerant trees and shrubs that few botanical gardens can grow outdoors.

Rainfall averages 22 inches per year, and more than 16 of these inches fall during five months from the beginning of November to the end of March. In contrast, typically less than an inch of rain falls during the five-month period from early May through September.

Golden Gate Park has seen great changes since its origins in the 1870s (page 79). Similarly, the Garden has undergone steady development since its opening in 1940 (page 83). Both Park and Garden have historically been and will continue to be works in progress. Trees planted during the late 1800s and early 1900s have reached maturity and in some cases are nearing the end of their life spans. Shrubs and perennials with short life cycles are continuously replaced with new plants. Each few years bring newly designed gardens and an ever-changing collection of plants to the Garden. Every season ushers in new sights and experiences.

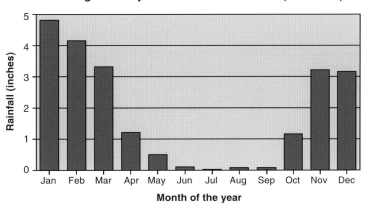

Average Monthly Rainfall in San Francisco (1971–2000)

Average monthly rainfall chart.

Be Prepared for Summer Fog

The daily retreat and advance of fog on typical summer days is fascinating for residents and visitors alike. Mornings often find the entire city covered by cool fog that gradually retreats, leaving the bay side of the city warm and sunny. The Garden is on the ocean side of San Francisco and remains foggy longer, and occasionally, temperatures remain cool for the entire day. The moving boundary between fog and sunshine is marked by gusty winds, leaving a relative calm in its wake.

For a summer visit, it is best to be prepared for either fog or sun. Temperatures can change by more than 25°F in a few minutes, and you can stay comfortable by switching between a jacket and short sleeves. Cool weather is often welcome when the weather map shows that nearby temperatures are in the 90s or above.

The lush green look of the Garden would not be possible without a reliable water supply, especially during the almost rain-free summer half of the year. Fortunately, over two-thirds of the water required for Golden Gate Park and the Garden is supplied by wells located in the central and western parts of the Park. Less than one-third comes from the municipal water system, which supplies mainly the museums, plant nurseries, drinking fountains, restrooms, and buildings that house offices, classrooms, and exhibit halls.

ABOVE: Gazebo in fog and rain [JOANNE TAYLOR]; OPPOSITE PAGE: Japanese maple in fall color [SAXON HOLT].

ENTRANCES

Two entrances welcome visitors to the Garden, the **Main Gate** and the **Friend Gate**. A ten-minute walk is all it takes to get from one gate to the other.

MAIN GATE

At the Main Gate, the Entry Garden offers a display of subtropical and temperate plants from around the world. Just beyond, the Great Meadow and central fountain come into view.

Entry Garden

The Entry Garden was planted in 1998. Plants were chosen for their bold shapes, varied textures, and unusual leaf forms. Dense plantings allow for few empty spaces. Ceramic planters, sculptures, and monastery stones (page 78) are half hidden among the luxuriant vegetation. The long planting bed on the bookstore side has a south-facing, sunny exposure where succulents, banana plants, New Zealand flax, and silver trees thrive. Of the hundreds of species concentrated here, many plants are new to the Garden. Some are considered experimental because they may not survive rare record-breaking frosts.

To the right of the bookstore is a relic of San Francisco's past, a large, bowl-shaped stone planter that once provided water for horses on Market Street. On the other side of the lawn panel, a ceramic gnome reads a book among the shade-loving plants around the Library Gate. Near the Great Meadow, a circular rock garden is dedicated to longtime (1979-1999) Garden Director Walden Valen.

PRECEEDING SPREAD: **Steps in Succulent Garden** [SAXON HOLT]; OPPOSITE: **Entry Garden** [SAXON HOLT]; THIS PAGE, TOP: *Aloe polyphylla*; THIS PAGE, BOTTOM: **Yucca and phormium** [SAXON HOLT].

Visitor Information

The **Main Gate** provides the most information for first-time visitors. Nearby signs display a map of the Garden and outline its history. The **Helen Crocker Russell Library** houses an excellent horticultural collection and exhibits botanical art that is for sale and benefits the library. A receptionist in the Library answers questions and welcomes visitors to enjoy the benefits of joining the **San Francisco Botanical Garden Society**. The **Garden Bookstore** is stocked with a varied selection of horticulture, botany, and natural history books.

Offices, classrooms, and exhibit halls occupy the building next to the Main Gate. This is where **courses** and **special lectures** are given and periodic **plant sales** are held. Further information about courses, events, and **volunteer opportunities** is posted inside the Main Gate and can be obtained at the office of the **Public Programs Department**.

Plant Sales

The Garden's sales feature many unusual plants that are not available elsewhere. The main **spring plant sale** is held in early May and is a magnet for home gardeners. Volunteers provide expert advice and serve refreshments. The first evening of the sale is held on a Friday and is reserved for members of the San Francisco Botanical Garden Society, but non-members are welcomed to join the Society and take advantage of this pre-sale. Smaller plant sales are held periodically throughout the year.

Docent-Guided Walks

Docent volunteers give **free daily tours** starting in front of the bookstore at the Main Gate. Additional tours start at the Friend Gate. Information about special walks, such as bird walks and moonlight walks, is posted at the entry gates and on the web site: www.sfbotanicalgarden.org.

OPPOSITE PAGE: *Flora, Mask of Leaves*. Sculpture in the North Entry bed by Maria Donohue.

FRIEND GATE

The Friend Gate is named in honor of Eugene L. Friend, emeritus president of the Recreation and Park Commission and a longtime supporter of the Garden. Also known as the North Gate, it is located near the rapidly changing part of Golden Gate Park facing the Music Concourse. Noted architects are rebuilding the two nearby museums using innovative designs. The de Young Museum, a fine arts museum, is reopening in 2005, and the California Academy of Sciences, the natural history museum, is projected for completion in 2008. An underground garage is being built between the two museums and near the Friend Gate, where it will provide parking for Park visitors. The Japanese Tea Garden across the street from the Friend Gate remains a popular attraction during the construction phase.

Information about coming events, courses, and volunteer opportunities is posted inside the Friend Gate. Nearby signs display a map of the Garden and outline its history. From the Gate, there is an inviting view of a sloping meadow down to the Wildfowl Pond. The central fountain beyond the pond points toward the Main Gate, which is a ten-minute walk away. After crossing the bridge across the Wildfowl Pond, turn left and walk uphill past the fountain. The Main Gate and the Library come into view beyond the Great Meadow.

ABOVE: **View from the Friend Gate** [JOANNE TAYLOR].

Reading Plant Labels

Labels throughout the Garden use a system of botanical names to identify plants by genus and species. A **species** is made up of plants that can interbreed to produce similar fertile offspring, and a **genus** is a group of related species. A group of related genera (plural of genus) makes up a **family** of plants. Some plant labels identify the subspecies, variety, or name of a garden selection. **Common names** in English and/or a language of the plant's native country are also included. Symbols indicate the special status of a plant, for example an **E** for a plant that is endangered in the wild.

Plant Names in this Guide

The familiar English common name, if there is one, is listed first and is followed by the botanical name: **Chilean bellflower** (*Lapageria rosea*). Common names in another language are in small capitals: **Chilean bellflower**, COPIHUE (*Lapageria rosea*). If there is no familiar common name, and in many cases there isn't, only the botanical name is listed.

THREE WALKS

THE TURN

In the 1870s, The Turn was a cul-de-sac where families on a horse-and-buggy outing to Golden Gate Park would turn around to return to the city. The location of The Turn is now in the part of Garden between the Main Gate and the Friend Gate, and its name is a reminder of the Park's early history.

This walk first circles the **Great Meadow** and then continues, making side trips into the **Demonstration**, **Fragrance**, **Rhododendron**, **Primitive Plant**,

OPPOSITE: Monterey cypress (*Cupressus macrocarpa*) [SAXON HOLT].

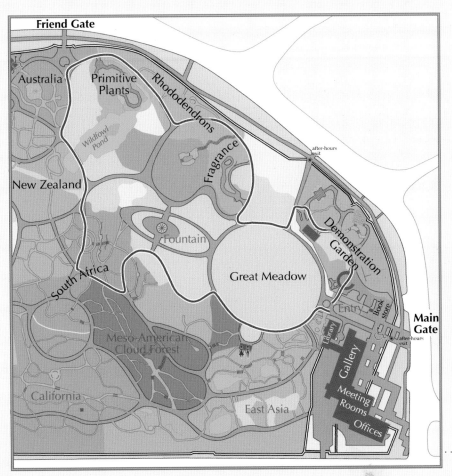

Friend Gate

Australia
Primitive Plants
Rhododendrons
Wildfowl Pond
Fragrance
New Zealand
after-hours exit
South Africa
Fountain
Demonstration Garden
Great Meadow
Meso-American Cloud Forest
Entry
Book store
Library
Main Gate
after-hours exit
Gallery
California
Meeting Rooms
East Asia
Offices

and **South Africa gardens**. It is a leisurely walk of about 45 minutes, which begins and ends at the Main Gate.

1. Great Meadow

The walk along the Great Meadow leads through an open landscape with long views to the central fountain and surrounding trees. The most prominent trees are Monterey cypress, Monterey pine, and blue gum eucalyptus. They were first planted throughout Golden Gate Park in the 1870s to provide shelter from the westerly winds off the Pacific Ocean and to stabilize the sand dunes. All three kinds of trees are fast growing and still provide essential wind protection.

Monterey pine (*Pinus radiata*) has a dense dome-like crown. Its abundant, fist-sized cones may remain closed and attached to larger branches for years. In the Garden, the tree grows much taller than it does in the wild along the Central California coast, south of San Francisco. The five-inch-long needles grow in bundles of three, and the gray-brown bark has deep vertical fissures. Replanting Monterey pines is problematic because some of these trees are becoming infected by pitch canker, an often-fatal fungal disease. Tree specialists are experimenting with disease-resistant strains that would have an improved chance of survival.

Monterey cypress (*Cupressus macrocarpa*) has broadly spreading, almost horizontal branches with dense, scaly foliage. The round walnut-sized cones grow in clusters, and the gray bark has closely spaced vertical fissures. Monterey cypress is native only to a small area just south of the Monterey Peninsula, where it is threatened. In Golden Gate Park, many of these trees are nearing the end of their natural life span. As they age, the centers of their trunks and their taproots are prone to decay, and they become more easily toppled by winter storms.

Eucalyptus globulus is known as blue gum in its native Australia. It has long,

sickle-shaped leaves that have a pungent fragrance. The leaves hang vertically and allow dappled sunlight to reach the ground underneath. The woody fruit is one inch in diameter with a cross-shaped opening on its lower surface. The smooth, pale gray bark sheds in long strips, exposing a light tan surface underneath. Blue

Central fountain.

gum tends to spread by seed if not carefully controlled.

The large open space of the Great Meadow with its undulating contours and central fountain was part of the 1959 Master Plan designed by Robert Tetlow, professor of landscape architecture at the University of California, Berkeley. The next part of this walk, the Demonstration Garden, shows the work of other local landscape designers.

2. Demonstration Garden

You can enter the two-acre Demonstration Garden from the circular rock garden near the Main Gate. The garden was completed in 1965 with the support of William Lane Jr., then publisher of *Sunset* magazine. In its early days, the Demonstration Garden had changing displays of plants that helped home gardeners decide which varieties to purchase for home use. The garden still provides take-home ideas by showing classic 1960s work of leading San Francisco-based landscape architects such as Thomas D. Church and Lawrence Halprin.

Thomas Church designed a partly shaded garden featuring a gazebo that sits on a raised wooden deck. An approach to the deck crosses two bridges over a dry creek. Plantings are informally arranged and rely on drought-tolerant plants that are appropriate to San Francisco's climate. Among the prominent shrubs is the pincushion protea *Leucospermum* 'Scarlet Ribbon', a spring-blooming native of South Africa. There is also a bank of sageleaf rockrose (*Cistus salvifolius*), a low-growing Mediterranean shrub that is covered in spring by masses of small white flowers with yellow at the base of the petals.

TOP: Garden by Thomas Church; MIDDLE: Pincushion protea (*Leucospermum* 'Scarlet Ribbon'); BOTTOM: Sageleaf rockrose (*Cistus salvifolius*).

Lawrence Halprin designed a hillside garden that leads to an elevated observation terrace. Steps of railroad ties climb the hill, which is thickly planted with bear's breech (*Acanthus mollis*), a perennial with large, shiny, deeply lobed leaves. The bold pattern of the leaves inspired the classic design at the top of Corinthian columns in ancient Greece. The right side of the slope is covered by large Mediterranean spurge (*Euphorbia characias*), a perennial shrub with narrow blue-green leaves and clusters of lime green flowers that bloom in late winter. The large eucalyptus trees with boldly patterned peeling trunks are known as manna gum (*Eucalyptus viminalis*) and shade the adobe brick terrace. Halprin, still active at age 88, is known for his designs of Levi Plaza in San Francisco and the Franklin D. Roosevelt Memorial in Washington, D.C.

The **Jean Wolff** Garden of white-flowering plants was opened in 1988. Wolff was a Bay Area designer of small city and suburban gardens, known for her creative use of plants that provide white blossoms all year long. This garden is designed in her memory and in her distinctive style. The gazebo and the carved benches are inviting and appropriate in scale. In late winter, white azaleas and

TOP: Lawrence Halprin Garden with *Eucalyptus viminalis* trunks on the right and bear's breech (*Acanthus mollis*) in the foreground; ABOVE LEFT: Mediterranean spurge (*Euphorbia characias*); RIGHT: Japanese snowball (*Viburnum plicatum* 'Summer Snowflake') in the Jean Wolff Garden; OPPOSITE PAGE: the Jean Wolff Garden.

Helleborus bloom behind the low sheared hedges. White flowering cherry blossoms appear in spring, and a tall shrub of Japanese snowball (*Viburnum plicatum* 'Summer Snowflake') is prominent in early summer.

After leaving the Demonstration Garden, continue along the Great Meadow to the Garden of Fragrance, a collection of plants with aromatic foliage or flowers.

3. Garden of Fragrance

The Fragrance Garden was designed in 1965 especially for people with impaired vision, but it proved to be just as popular with the general public. There are raised beds behind limestone retaining walls, which make it easy for children and visitors

in wheelchairs to touch the fragrant foliage. The garden was renovated in 1982 with help from Ikebana International and again in 2005.

A light brush of the hand against the foliage of many plants will pick up their distinct fragrances. The sound of water comes from a bronze statue of St. Francis, patron saint of San Francisco and protector of plants and animals. The trickle of water feeds a small pond near the retaining wall. The water, nearby berries and flowers, and the quiet wind-protected location prove to be an irresistible attraction for birds.

The mint family is prominent in this garden and includes many **culinary herbs** from around the Mediterranean Sea. Rosemary, thyme, lavender, sage, and mint are not only useful in the kitchen, they are also good deer- and rabbit-resistant choices for country

OPPOSITE: Lemon verbena (*Aloysia triphylla*) on left and lemon geranium (*Pelargonium crispum*); THIS PAGE, ABOVE LEFT: St. Francis statue [SAXON HOLT]; RIGHT, TOP TO BOTTOM: Luculia (*Luculia intermedia*); Common myrtle (*Myrtus communis*); Mexican bush sage (*Salvia leucantha*).

and suburban gardens: the aromas that appeal to people tend to repel browsing animals. Sage belongs to the genus *Salvia*, which includes about 900 species from many parts of the world. **Mexican bush sage** (*Salvia leucantha*) with its aromatic leaves and velvety purple flowers is a familiar example.

Lavender cotton has foliage with a pungent fragrance. The species with bright green leaves is *Santolina virens*, and the one with gray foliage is *Santolina chamaecyparissus*. The shrubs are in the daisy family and bloom in late spring and summer with hundreds of small, button-sized, yellow flowers.

Lemon verbena (*Aloysia triphylla*) is among the larger shrubs. Touch the leaves to enjoy the intense lemon fragrance on your fingers. This deciduous plant is native to Chile and Argentina, where the leaves are used to make tea. The South African **lemon geranium** (*Pelargonium crispum*) is a broadleaf evergreen perennial with foliage that also releases a refreshing lemon scent.

Common myrtle (*Myrtus communis*) is an evergreen shrub from the lands around the Mediterranean Sea. The glossy evergreen leaves have a pleasant aroma. Small, fragrant white flowers with many male stamens appear in the summer. In ancient times, they were a symbol of peace and love.

Luculia intermedia is a large shrub that is a native of China. Its pale pink flowers have an intense sweet fragrance that is especially noticeable during the late summer and fall peak of a long blooming season.

After leaving the Garden of Fragrance, the Rhododendron Garden comes into view as you continue on The Turn. This garden features a single genus of plants.

TOP: Lavender cotton (*Santolina chamaecyparissus*); BOTTOM: Lemon geraneum (*Pelargonium crispum*) to the right of an historic bell [JOANNE TAYLOR].

4. Rhododendron Garden

The Rhododendron Garden grows on a north-facing hillside in the filtered shade of tall trees. Originally, the soil was sandy. Since rhododendrons require a moisture-holding soil rich in organic matter, generous amounts of soil amendments were added to prepare the garden for its first plantings from the 1940s to the 1960s. This garden was designed to suggest a woodland landscape.

The genus *Rhododendron* includes roughly 1,000 species, of which about three-quarters are native to southwestern China and the eastern Himalayas. However, rhododendrons also originated in North America, Central Asia, and all of eastern Asia between Siberia and New Guinea. They are a diverse group of plants, which includes azaleas.

Rhododendrons have a more than 1,500-year history as garden plants in China. This garden is noted for its collection of **Arborea** and **Maddenii** rhododendrons, two Southeast Asian subgroups that require mild winters. These rhododendrons also benefit from San Francisco's cool moist fog from May to August, when the plants produce new foliage.

Many of the large tree-like rhododendrons of the **Arborea** group are on the slope of the hill to the left of the path. They are named for *Rhododendron arboreum*, which is native to the eastern Himalayas and was first sent to England in 1811. This species has many naturally occurring varieties, but those with

large clusters of red flowers are most prized. *Rhododendron arboreum* could not survive outdoors in England's winter cold except in the mildest coastal locations. But nurserymen and wealthy amateurs were soon successful in crossing it with

TOP TO BOTTOM: *Rhododendron arboreum*; R. 'Honeysuckle'; *R. maddenii*.

the more cold-tolerant *Rhododendron catawbiense* from America's Appalachian Mountains. The hybrids included many with spectacular blossoms in rich shades of red and pink that were more frost-tolerant. This early success in hybridization started a period of experimentation that produced many offspring. An example is *Rhododendron* 'John McLaren', that blooms from mid-winter through mid-spring. It is named in honor of San Francisco's park superintendent from 1987 to 1943.

Rhododendrons of the **Maddenii** group grow at the base of the hill. These medium-sized shrubs have fragrant white flowers tinted with pink or yellow. Maddenii rhododendrons are even more frost-sensitive than the Arboreum group, and in most botanical gardens they can only be grown in greenhouses. This garden has one of the best outdoor collections of Maddenii rhododendrons in North

America. In the subtropical rainforest of Southeast Asia, *Rhododendron maddenii* lives on tree branches as an epiphyte. In cultivation, it is usually grown as a shrub. This species was first collected by the noted botanist Sir Joseph Hooker and introduced to British horticulture shortly after 1849. Later, *Rhododendron maddenii* was widely used for hybridization, especially in California, and is the ancestor of many fragrant and colorful offspring such as *Rhododendron fragrantissimum*.

Look for other plants from East Asia in this garden. Those that flower in summer include false spiraea (*Astilbe chinensis*) in shades of red, pink, and white, Japanese anemones (*Anemone* x hybrida) with tall-stemmed flowers

THIS PAGE, TOP: *Rhododendron* 'Noyo Chief'; BOTTOM: False spiraea (*Astilbe chinensis*) in late summer; OPPOSITE PAGE: *R.* 'Noyo Chief'.

of white or pink with yellow centers, and fragrant yellow ginger (*Hedychium flavescens*).

For a view of the central fountain, the Great Meadow, the Main Gate, and the setting of the Garden in the Inner Sunset district of the city, follow the path to the left with steps that lead to the top of the hill. Among the Arborea rhododendrons on the hillside are magnolia trees that bloom in January and February, a tall pink-flowering *Magnolia campbellii* and a white *Magnolia denudata*. The hill has been known as **Heidelberg Hill** since the California Midwinter International Exposition of

1894, when a "German village" with a castle facade and beer garden was built on the hilltop.

The Rhododendron Garden was renovated in 2005. A pavilion with interpretive signs introduces the genus, describes its distribution in the world, and provides advice on cultivation. New plantings emphasize rhododendrons that were originally native to East Asia. There is also an increased number of magnolias, maples, and understory plants from that part of the world.

Other azaleas and rhododendrons can be seen in the Moon-Viewing, Southeast Asian Cloud Forest, California, East Asia, and Library Terrace gardens on the Collections Trail (page 57).

After you leave the Rhododendron Garden, the Primitive Plant Garden, located to the left, traces the evolution of plants.

5. Primitive Plant Garden

The Primitive Plant Garden opened in 1994. It begins at a bench-lined entry deck with two large interpretive signs that illustrate the evolution of plants. A raised boardwalk to the left begins a short loop through the garden. Small signs are arranged chronologically, starting with blue-green bacteria and algae, which were the earliest plants to evolve about 3,500 million years ago, and ending with early flowering plants, whose ancestors arose around 140 million years ago.

The displays emphasize the earliest groups of upright plants to establish themselves on land. These include relatives of ferns that date back 400 million years,

OPPOSITE, TOP: Magnolia (*Magnolia cambellii*); OPPOSITE, BOTTOM: Yulan magnolia (*Magnolia denudata*). THIS PAGE, ABOVE LEFT: Japanese anemone (*Anemone* x hybrida); ABOVE RIGHT: Yellow ginger (*Hedychium flavescens*).

along with horsetails, conifers, cycads, and ginkgos that originated between 200 and 300 million years ago. Flowering plants evolved more recently, about 140 million years ago during the age of dinosaurs.

Ferns and horsetails were among the first land plants to develop true roots, stems, and leaves. They have two systems of vessels, one of which transports water and minerals from the roots to other parts of the plant. The other system distributes the nutrients that are produced in the leaves and stems by photosynthesis, a process that uses energy from sunlight. Ferns and horsetails both reproduce by making an enormous number of tiny spores, which are dispersed by the wind. The tree ferns in this garden come from moist climates with moderate temperatures. They include *Dicksonia squarrosa* and *Cyathea medullaris* from New Zealand and *Cyathea cooperi* and *Dicksonia antarctica* from coastal eastern Aus-

TOP: Entry deck with interpretive signs and rough tree ferns (*Cyathea cooperi*); OPPOSITE, CLOCKWISE FROM TOP LEFT: Horsetails (*Equisetum giganteum*) growing in a bed of *Equisetum scirpoides*; One of many tree ferns; Norfolk Island pine (*Araucaria heterophylla*) foliage.

tralia. A look at the underside of larger fronds reveals small circular sacs that produce an abundance of dark powdery spores.

Conifers are among the earliest seed-bearing plants, with a history that extends back about 300 million years. About 550 species of conifers still survive and even dominate the northern forests of North America, Europe, and Asia. Most have needle-like or scale-like leaves and bear pollen and seeds in separate male and female cones. Conifer fossils are preserved in coal beds, which are the remains of ancient forests. Conifers grown in this garden include California's coast redwood (*Sequoia sempervirens*) (page 69), which once flourished throughout much of the Northern Hemisphere. Norfolk Island pine (*Araucaria heterophylla*) belongs to a group of conifers widely distributed in the Southern Hemisphere. In contrast to abundant conifer species, the maidenhair tree (*Ginkgo biloba*) is the only surviving example of its ancient genus.

The diversity and success of **flowering plants** that dominate the plant world today are due in large part to their beneficial interaction with pollinators such as

bees, butterflies, beetles, birds, and bats, which co-evolved during the same period. Pollinators benefit the plants by efficiently carrying pollen to fertilize the female parts of other flowers. The pollinators are motivated by the prospect of a sweet and nutritious meal of nectar and pollen.

Flowers of the magnolia family share many of the characteristics of early flowering plants, such as petals that are spirally arranged and separated from one another. Near the end of the boardwalk, look for other flowers with this characteristic, including *Helleborus argutifolius* in winter and spring, buttercups (*Ranunculus* species) in spring, spice bush (*Calycanthus occidentalis*) in summer, and Japanese anemones (*Anemone* x hybrida) in late summer and early fall.

After leaving the Primitive Plant Garden, continue on The Turn toward the Friend Gate. Then bear left to the Wildfowl Pond, passing the Australia and New Zealand gardens which are part of the Garden Walk (page 45). Cross the bridge over the Wildfowl Pond and bear right to reach the South Africa Garden. This garden displays plants from a distant part of the world that enjoys a mediterranean climate.

THIS PAGE, TOP TO BOTTOM: Corsican helebore (*Helleborus argutifolius*); Spice bush (*Calycanthus occidentalis*); Japanese anemone (*Anemone* x hybrida).

6. South Africa Garden

The South Africa Garden is one of four gardens devoted to plants and landscapes of countries situated in the Southern Hemisphere. It was designed and planted in 1985 with support of the San Francisco Botanical Garden Society. A feature of the garden is a west-facing slope terraced with three semicircular planting beds separated by paths and waist-high stone retaining walls. The walls retain the sun's heat and transfer it to the planting beds behind them. Benches on the paths provide wind protection and, in fair weather, invite visitors to bask in the sun.

The vegetation of South Africa is unusually varied, including many plants unfamiliar to gardeners in the Northern Hemisphere. Most of the plants in the garden are native to the southwestern tip of South Africa near the city of Cape Town. This small area has a mediterranean climate of dry summers and mild wet winters, similar to that of lands around the Mediterranean Sea, and

Steps to the semicircular terraces.

parts of California, Chile and Australia. The climate of metropolitan Cape Town is particularly close to that of the San Francisco Bay Area in having summer fog

that helps plants survive the dry season. This garden illustrates how a distinctive group of African plants can thrive in the similar climate of San Francisco.

How plants survive in dry summers. Plants growing in any mediterranean climate have to be able to live through the long, almost rain-free summers. They have evolved various adaptations that promote survival during this stressful season.

Protea shrubs are South Africa's most famous flowering plants. The genus *Protea* is known for its large blossoms, each of which is made up of hundreds of tiny, individual flowers surrounded by brightly colored bracts or modified leaves. The largest, with blossoms ten inches across, is South Africa's

TOP: King protea (*Protea cynaroides*) [JOANNE TAYLOR]; BOTTOM LEFT: Wand flower (*Dierama pulcherrima*); BOTTOM RIGHT: *Crocosmia masoniorum*.

floral symbol, the king protea (*Protea cynaroides*). In a related genus, the pincushion proteas include *Leucospermum* 'Tottum Hybrid'. Both bloom in spring and have thick, leathery evergreen leaves that conserve water.

Heathers are evergreen shrubs in the genus *Erica*. They have needle-like leaves that hold on to moisture. The small, colorful flowers are shaped like urns, bells, or long curved tubes. The urn-shaped *Erica canaliculata* blooms in winter and early spring, and the tube-shaped *Erica blanda* flowers in fall.

Aloes, such as the winter-blooming tree aloe (*Aloe arborea*), have thick fleshy leaves that store enormous amounts of water that maintain them during the dry season.

South Africa has a great variety of **geophytes** or **bulbs**. Bulbs survive summer drought by storing food and water underground. In the iris family, *Crocosmia masoniorum* flowers in spring, and the arching wand

TOP RIGHT: Tree aloe (*Aloe arborea*); BOTTOM LEFT: Pincushion protea (*Leucospermum* 'Tottum Hybrid'); BOTTOM RIGHT: Lily of the Nile (*Agapanthus africanus*).

flowers (*Dierama pulcherrima*) blossom in summer. In the amaryllis family, *Haemanthus coccinea* blooms in the fall. The leaves emerge after the flowers and stay green through the winter.

South African plants in California. Plants from South Africa were being sold to Northern California gardeners within five years of the Gold Rush. A San Francisco nursery was offering lily of the Nile (*Agapanthus africanus*) and many kinds of ivy geraniums and scented geraniums (*Pelargonium* species), and a Sacramento nursery listed the bird of paradise plant (*Strelitzia reginae*) in its 1853 catalog. Since then, increasing numbers of South African plants have become available to California gardeners. Many are excellent choices for water-conserving gardens in the Bay Area and elsewhere in California west of the Sierra Nevada.

For more about this garden, see the Garden Walk on page 51.

To Complete The Turn, walk through the South Africa Garden toward the central fountain and the Great Meadow. In mid-spring, don't miss the crabapples including *Malus* 'Liset', that are in bloom near the fountain. Each gate is about five minutes away. The **Main Gate** is in view on the far side of the Great Meadow; the **Friend Gate** is reached by continuing around the Great Meadow on The Turn.

ABOVE: Bird of paradise plant (*Strelitzia reginae*); BELOW: Crabapples (*Malus* 'Liset') in late March and early April [SAXON HOLT].

THE GARDEN WALK

The **Garden Walk** starts at the Friend Gate and winds through the central part of the Gardens. It begins with a visit to three Southern Hemisphere gardens: **Australia**, **New Zealand**, and **South Africa** and is followed by the **Meso-American Cloud Forest**, returning to the Friend Gate by way of the Great Meadow. The walk takes around 45 minutes at a relaxed pace.

From the **Friend Gate**, a welcoming view of the sloping meadow down to the Wildfowl Pond and the central fountain in the distance greets the visitor. The Australia Garden is located just inside the Friend Gate.

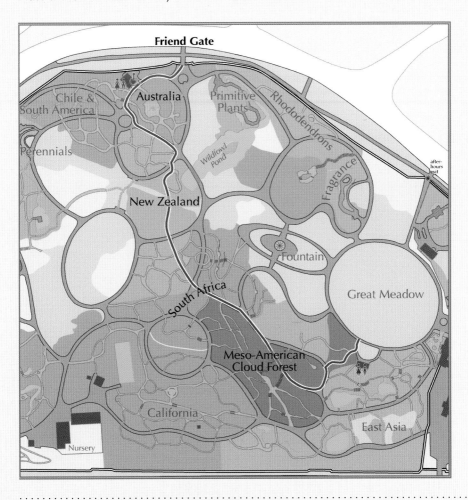

1. Australia Garden

A variety of Australian shrubs and perennials is displayed in a raised **circular rock garden** near the Friend Gate. As you face the Wildfowl Pond, the garden to the right was designed by Bernard Traynor and was planted in 2004. Its three sculp-

tural retaining walls near a dry creek give the plantings a feeling of Traynor's native Australian landscapes.

Many of the shrubs and trees in this garden belong to three groups of plants that dominate the vegetation of Australia: the myrtle, protea, and pea families.

- **Eucalyptus** trees with smooth trunks and peeling bark, that Australians refer to as gums, are representatives of the **myrtle family**. A snow gum (*Eucalyptus pauciflora*) stands to the right of the Friend Gate. This broadleaf evergreen tree has striking white branching trunks with irregular strips of peeling bark. The strap-like leaves hang vertically, allowing them to avoid the drying effects of direct sunlight. Large clusters of flowers cover the tree in summer.

Various kinds of **bottlebrush** are also in the myrtle family. Most of these are large broadleaf evergreen shrubs or small trees with cylindrical flower clusters. The compound flowers have a brush-like appearance made up of hundreds of stamens, the bristle-like male parts of the flowers. Look for the bright red blossoms of the lemon-scented bottlebrush (*Callistemum citrinus*) and the pale yellow lemon bottlebrush (*Callistemum pallidus*). Woody clusters of seeds from the flower clusters of previous years remain attached closer to the base of the stems.

- Many of Australia's most striking shrubs and small trees are members of the **protea family**. Among the best known of these are banksias and grevilleas. **Banksias** have large cylindrical blossoms made up of a spiral arrangement of hundreds of individual

TOP: Lemon-scented bottlebrush (*Callistemum citrinus*); BOTTOM: Hairpin banksia (*Banksia spinulosa*).

flowers. Two examples are hairpin banksia (*Banksia spinulosa*) and woolly orange banksia (*Banksia victoriae*).

Grevilleas have curved tubular red flowers that are visited by hummingbirds. These shrubs are particularly popular in California gardens. Among the grevilleas on this walk are *Grevillea* 'Pink Pearl' and *Grevillea lanigera* 'Mt. Tamboritha'.

- The **pea family** includes Australia's roughly 900 species of acacia and a large number of its vines. Tough seedpods are found on many plants in this family. In Australia, **acacias** are commonly known as wattles. Silver wattle (*Acacia podalyriifolia*) is a small tree with silvery blue-green foliage. Like many acacias, it blooms in winter or early spring with clusters of bright yellow flowers that consist of a puff of male stamens about 1/4 inch in diameter.

Near the restrooms are two notable trees. The **Moreton Bay fig** (*Ficus macrophylla*) has large thick shiny leaves. The **lilly pilly tree** (*Acmena smithii*) bears abundant purple-pink fruit with a bland-tasting soft white pulp. Both trees are from tropical and subtropical eastern Australia.

Where the Australia Garden meets Gondwana Circle, look for a group of **rough tree ferns** (*Cyathea cooperi*). The trunks are erect with fronds at the top. The fern is easy to grow and can tolerate not only deep shade but also full sun if it is well watered. In southeastern Australia it often grows in moist, shaded gullies and can reach heights of 40 feet.

TOP: Silver wattle (*Acacia podalyriifolia*); ABOVE LEFT: *Grevillea lanigera* 'Mt. Tamboritha'; ABOVE RIGHT: Stream lily (*Helmholzia gluberina*).

The New Zealand garden begins on the right as you continue toward the Wildfowl Pond from Gondwana Circle.

2. New Zealand Garden

Australia and New Zealand are about 1,000 miles apart. But about 60 million years ago, they were very close to one another and to Antarctica. At that time, Antarctica had a mild climate, as evidenced by fossil plants that resemble those now growing in Australia and New Zealand. The one-time contact of these landmasses in a giant continent named Gondwana helps explain why southern beech trees (*Nothofagus*), tea trees (*Leptospermum*), tree ferns, and many other kinds of plants grow in both Australia and New Zealand.

New Zealand's North Island and South Island stretch out over a distance of almost 1,000 miles, almost the north-south distance between Seattle and Los Angeles. The islands have a mild, ocean-moderated climate with year-round rainfall. New Zealand plants thrive in San Francisco's similarly mild climate, but require periodic watering to tide them over during the summer dry season.

New Zealand Christmas tree POHUTUKAWA (*Metrosiderus excelsa*).

West Coast gardeners will notice many familiar trees and shrubs that are valued as landscaping for their interesting foliage and shapes. Colorful flowers, which attract insect pollinators, are not prominent among New Zealand plants. This is probably related to the scarcity of insect pollinators before European settlers introduced bees in the 19th century. The few brightly colored shrubs and trees, like the red New Zealand Christmas tree, are likely to be pollinated by birds.

The first settlers of New Zealand were the Maori, a Polynesian people who arrived about 1,000 years ago. Many New Zealand plants are still known by their Maori names, which are identified here by small capital letters.

A large **New Zealand Christmas tree** POHUTUKAWA (*Metrosiderus excelsa*) grows at the near side of the bridge across the Wildfowl Pond. This broad tree is supported by many extra trunks, which form after aerial roots reach and then enter the ground. In New Zealand, the tree blooms with bright red flowers during Christmas time, which is early summer in the Southern Hemisphere. In San Francisco, the tree flowers in June.

From the bridge across the Wildfowl Pond there is a view of a grove of New Zealand's only palm tree, the **Nikau palm** (*Rhopalostylis sapida*). In the wild, they grow further from the equator than any other palm species in the world.

Nearby is a new grove of **black tree fern** MAMAKU (*Cyathea medullaris*), New Zealand's tallest tree fern. Mature plants can reach a height of 65 feet.

The **cabbage tree**, TI (*Cordyline australis*) is a common street tree in California. The spongy, cork-like trunk has branches that end with clusters of strap-like leaves. Clumps of white flowers bloom in late spring.

Tea trees, MANUKA (*Leptospermum scoparium*) grow in several parts of this garden. They have short, needle-like foliage and the small white, pink, or red

TOP: New Zealand Christmas tree flower; MIDDLE: Tea tree, MANUKA (*Leptospermum scoparium*); BOTTOM: *Hebe* sp.

flowers with five petals bloom for much of the year, with a peak in spring and summer.

Totara (*Podocarpus totara*) is a tall New Zealand conifer with a straight, thick trunk. *Podocarpus* is a genus with origins in the ancient continent of Gondwana, and is native to Australia, New Zealand, and Chile.

Hebes and phormiums are two more groups of New Zealand plants that have become popular with West Coast gardeners. **Hebes** are evergreen shrubs with abundant clusters of purple, violet, blue, or white flowers. They are widely grown in parts of coastal California that have a mild summer and no more than a rare light frost in winter. **New Zealand flax** (*Phormium tenax*) has stiff, sword-shaped leaves. There are many hybrids with leaf patterns of green, striped along their length with yellow, red, purple, or bronze.

Importance of Botanical Names

Plant specialists and amateurs use botanical names because they are internationally recognized. The botanical name avoids confusion when the same common name is used for entirely unrelated plants. An example is cabbage tree, a common name that is used in New Zealand and South Africa. The botanical name of New Zealand's cabbage tree is *Cordyline australis*, and it is in agave family. South Africa's cabbage tree is *Cussonia paniculata*, in the ivy and ginseng family.

Botanical names are also necessary to identify various kinds of manzanita and oak, whose common names refer to many different species.

Even California's state flower, the California poppy, is internationally recognized by its botanical name, *Eschscholzia californica*.

TOP: New Zealand flax (*Phormium tenax* 'Guardsman'); BOTTOM: South Africa's cabbage tree, *Cussonia paniculata*.

Adjacent to the New Zealand Garden is another representative of Southern Hemisphere flora, the South Africa Garden.

3. South Africa Garden

In the South Africa Garden, you can enjoy three groups of plants in the **Protea family**: the genus *Protea*, pincushion proteas, and sunshine proteas.

- The genus **Protea** is the most famous of South Africa's unusually rich and diverse plant life. The novelty of these plants, with their huge and varied blossoms, astounded European plant collectors in the 17th and 18th centuries, when they first visited the Cape Region of South Africa. Nothing similar existed among European plants. Proteas, which in most of Europe and North America can only be grown in greenhouses, still remain a novelty in California gardens. Some proteas in this garden will be in bloom during any part of the year, just as in the Cape Region of South Africa.

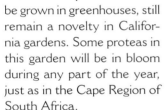

Oleander-leaved protea (*Protea neriifolia*) is a shrub with large colorful blossoms on display for much of the year. The resemblance of its leaves to the Mediterranean oleander (*Nerium oleander*), gives rise to the common name. Clusters of minute cream-colored flowers are packed inside pink and black-tipped bracts, or modified leaves.

- **Pincushion proteas** have colorful compound blossoms with bright rings of red, yellow, or orange styles (female flower parts) that look like circles

TOP: Oleander-leaved protea (*Protea nerifolia*); BOTTOM: Wheelflower (*Leucospermum catherinae*).

of curved pins. From late winter through spring, when these shrubs are in bloom, all floral stages from bud to fully opened blossoms are on display. An example of pincushion proteas is the wheelflower (*Leucospermum catherinae*), which blooms in spring.

- **Sunshine proteas** include the silver tree (*Leucadendron argenteum*), which is native to a small area in and near the city of Cape Town. It is recognized by its silvery leaves, which shine in the sunlight and shimmer in the wind. Touch the silky hairs that cover the leaves; these allow the plant to conserve water by reflecting light. The trees are frost-sensitive and grow best near the coast, where the temperature are mild. *Leucadendron* 'Cloud Bank Jenny' is in the same genus as the silver tree. It makes handsome and long lasting cut "flowers" with cream-colored leaf-like bracts and red centers.

For more about the South Africa Garden, see page 41.

Adjacent to the South Africa Garden is the Meso-American Cloud Forest, which is the last stop on the Garden Walk.

4. Meso-American Cloud Forest

The Meso-American Cloud Forest takes you into lush and shady surroundings. Cloud forests grow in the tropics, but because of their high elevations, between 6,000 and 12,000 feet, the mountain slopes are kept cool and moist by cloud cover and drizzle most of the day. There is typically a luxuriant growth of tall trees with an understory of smaller trees and shrubs. Abundant vines climb on trunks and branches to reach brighter light in the tree canopy. The forest floor is dimly lit due to the dense fog and the layers of foliage overhead. Many understory shrubs have broad, soft, velvety leaves in these moist and shady surroundings.

This garden was first planted in 1984 and provides a rare opportunity to see tropical plants that grow in remote, hard to reach, and rarely visited areas. Dr. Dennis Breedlove, a botanist with the California Academy of Sciences, collected most of the plants in southern Mexico over a 30-year period. Tropical cloud forest occupies a tiny percentage of the world's land area and is becoming threatened by the spread of logging and farming. Some plants growing in this garden have probably become extinct in the habitats where they were originally collected.

Plants from cloud forest surroundings do well in this garden because of

the similarly mild temperatures and moist summer fog. With extra watering during dry weather, the garden supports a rich outdoor collection of cloud forest plants. Vibrantly colored flowers are in bloom during any season. In fall and winter especially, tall tree daisies and tree dahlias catch the eye with their showy blooms.

OPPOSITE TOP: Silver tree (*Leucadendron argenteum*); OPPOSITE BOTTOM: *Leucadendron* ' Cloud Bank Jenny'; THIS PAGE: Cloud forest vines.

Tree daisies (*Montanoa leucantha* subspecies *arboreum*) are woody perennials that grow to a tree-like height of 20 feet that is highly unusual for the daisy family. Abundant clusters of fragrant white flowers serve as an attraction for monarch butterflies.

Tree dahlias (*Dahlia imperialis*) grow to heights of 15 feet or more after emerging from their tuberous roots. The daisy-like lavender flowers have yellow centers.

Many brightly colored salvias and fuchsias are in bloom at any season. **Salvias** are in the mint family. There are roughly 900 species worldwide, and Mexico boasts of more than any other country. Cloud forest salvias are notable for having brilliantly colored tubular flowers. The vivid blue *Salvia cacaliaefolia* and the deep red *Salvia gesnerifolia*, both of which bloom in spring and summer, are particularly striking. **Fuchsias** are extravagant in the variety of red, tubular flowers that they display over a long blooming season. Examples are *Fuchsia campos-portoi*, which

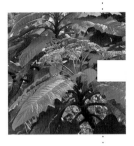

blooms in fall and winter, and *Fuchsia boliviana*, which flowers in summer and fall. Hummingbirds serve as pollinators for both salvias and fuchsias.

Mexican pine (*Pinus oaxacana*) is a graceful tree with thin, pliable needles that are soft to the touch and grow eight inches long. This is one of many distinctive pines native to Mexico.

Oxalis tetraphylla is a striking four-leaf clover with divided leaves that are green toward the edges and turn to dark purple where their segments join. Small pink flowers appear during the late spring.

Continue walking in the direction of the **Great Meadow** toward the upper part of the Meso-American Cloud Forest. This part of the garden provides the easiest access for visitors walking from the Main Gate and circling the Great Meadow. It showcases a wide variety of cloud forest shrubs, including the following:

Telanthophora grandifolia is a winter-blooming member of the daisy family with huge leaves and broad clusters of yellow flowers.

Deppea splendens is an attractive fall-blooming shrub that probably has become extinct in the wild. It produces clusters of two-inch-long yellow-orange tubular flowers and is a member of the coffee family.

The Garden Walk ends at the Great Meadow. From there, take **The Turn** along the Great Meadow for the two-minute walk to the **Main Gate** or return to the **Friend Gate** in about five minutes.

CLOCKWISE FROM OPPOSITE LEFT: Tree daisy (*Montanoa leucantha* subspecies *arboreum*); Tree daisy flowers; Tree dahlia (*Dahlia imperialis*); *Salvia cacaliaefolia*; *Salvia gesnerifolia*; *Fuchsia campos portoi*; *Telanthophora grandifolia*; Mexican pine (*Pinus oaxacana*); *Oxalis tetraphylla*.

THE COLLECTIONS TRAIL

The **Collections Trail** begins near the Friend Gate, leads through eight gardens, and ends near the Main Gate, from which a return to the Friend Gate takes about ten minutes. To start this walk, turn right at the circular rock garden inside the Friend Gate and continue walking past the restrooms to the Chile and South America Garden. The Collections Trail is the longest of the three walks and takes about an hour and a half at a relaxed pace.

This walk includes the **Chile and South America Garden**, the **Garden of Perennials**, the **Moon-Viewing Garden**, the **Southeast Asian Cloud Forest**, the **Succulent Garden**, the **Redwood Nature Trail**, the **California Garden**, and **East Asia Valley**.

1. Chile and South America

Many of the plants in the Chile and South America Garden are native to central Chile, which has a mediterranean climate similar to that of coastal

OPPOSITE: Chilean rhubarb (*Gunnera tinctoria*) [SAXON HOLT].

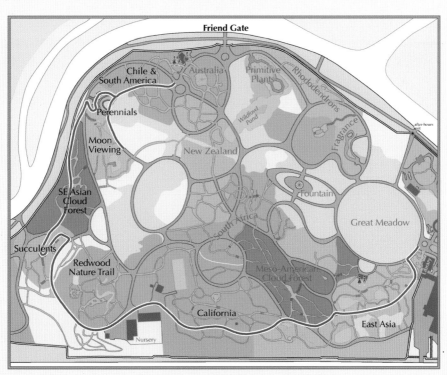

California. Interestingly, most of its plants are different, having evolved along independent paths. Parts of the garden also include plants that originate from the cool mountainous parts of tropical and subtropical South America.

Chilean rhubarb (*Gunnera tinctoria*, formerly *Gunnera chilensis*) is a perennial that displays huge leaves and a rapid rate of growth. The foliage dies down each winter, and a new crop of leaves unfolds in early spring. In Chile, young stalks are peeled and eaten as a vegetable. Mature leaves are rough-textured, more than five feet in diameter, and supported by thick, spiky stalks. In summer, large cone-like blossoms each bear hundreds of male or female flowers. The female spikes develop a spiral pattern of bright orange fruits that are the size and shape of tiny glass beads.

Alstroemeria is a genus that produces azalea-like flowers starting in spring and continuing

THIS PAGE, TOP: Darwin barberry (*Berberis darwinii*); BOTTOM LEFT: *Luma apiculata*; TOP RIGHT: *Luma* flowers; BOTTOM RIGHT: Winter's bark (*Drimys winteri*); OPPOSITE PAGE, TOP: Paraná pine (*Araucaria angustifolia*); BOTTOM: Marmalade bush (*Streptosolen jamesonii*).

throughout summer. The plants are easy to grow, and florists favor its flowers, which come in shades of yellow, orange, and red. *Alstroemeria* is closely related to the lily and iris families and similarly has fleshy roots.

Darwin barberry MICHAY (*Berberis darwinii*) was collected by Charles Darwin in 1835, when he was ship naturalist during the voyage of the *Beagle*. The shrub is popular for garden use, bearing abundant clusters of small, deep yellow to orange flowers. Dark blue berries ripen in the fall and are an irresistible attraction for birds.

ARAYÁN ROJO (*Luma apiculata*), is an easy-to-grow small broadleaf evergreen tree native to central Chile. The picturesque, twisted trunk has a distinctive red-brown peeling bark. In late summer, the tree is covered with small, white, fragrant flowers that have four petals surrounding a cluster of cream-colored male stamens. Dark blue, half-inch diameter berries mature in fall.

Chilean bellflower COPIHUE (*Lapageria rosea*) is an evergreen vine. Its three-inch-long fleshy red bell-shaped blossoms are Chile's national flower and bloom from late summer through autumn.

Winter's bark CANELO (*Drimys winteri*) bears clusters of white flowers on mahogany red stems. It is a sacred tree of Chile's Mapuche Indians and is used during healing ceremonies.

Azara serrata is an evergreen shrub with shiny dark green leaves. The fragrant bright yellow flowers are clustered at the end of a short thin stalk.

Conifers are relatively uncommon in the Southern Hemisphere, and most are quite different in appearance from conifers of the Northern Hemisphere. Many species have broad leaves instead of the familiar needles of the Northern Hemisphere's pines and spruces.

Paraná pine (*Araucaria angustifolia*) grows in southern Brazil and has tiers of drooping branches that emerge from a straight, knobby, elephant-gray trunk. The flat, inch-long leaves end in a sharp tip. The trees are either male or female. The specimen in this garden is a male tree.

Marmalade bush (*Streptosolen jamesii*) is native to the mountains of Ecuador. Orange and deep yellow flowers are in bloom for nearly the entire year.

Angel's trumpet (*Brugmansia* 'Inca Queen') is a large striking evergreen shrub that produces six inch long tubular flowers that hang vertically. All parts of the plant are poisonous if eaten. Angel's trumpets can be trained as small trees and have a long blooming season.

The Garden of Perennials is located next to the Chile and South America Garden and suggests the style of an estate garden.

2. Garden of Perennials

The Garden of Perennials enjoys long views of a meadow bordered by shrubs and trees. The central fountain in the distance points toward the Main Gate, which lies hidden below the line of vision. The garden was established in 1966 and redesigned in 2002 with support of the Zellerbach family.

A large central stone and cypress trellis is flanked by two smaller trellises. The plantings include rare and unusual perennials and shrubs, and some plants are in bloom during all seasons of the year. Groupings of the same variety create large, dense waves of texture and color.

TOP: View of meadow and central fountain from middle trellis; BOTTOM: Perennial beds being planted in 2002.

Beds of perennials and low-growing shrubs curve around a small semicircular lawn at the base of the garden. Behind the perennial beds are three trellises that are reached by an S-shaped wheelchair accessible stone path. The path is lined

with large bowl-shaped planters containing **New Zealand flax** (*Phormium* 'Cream Delight') and the sky blue flowers of **Corydalis flexuosa 'China Blue'**. The photos show a selection of perennials that were recently in bloom during early summer.

Taller border plants line the garden on each side. A hedge of **Escallonia x langleyensis 'Apple Blossom'** grows on the right side as you face the trellises. This dense evergreen shrub bears pinkish-white flowers from late spring through the fall. A **dogwood** (*Cornus* 'Eddie's White Wonder') blooms in late spring on the left, near the Moon-Viewing Garden.

Wisteria vines climb the three trellises, creating a white and lavender display in spring. Behind the trellises is a grove of

LEFT, TOP TO BOTTOM: Planters with New Zealand flax (*Phormium* 'Cream Delight') and sky blue flowers of *Corydalis flexuosa* 'China Blue'; *Trachelium* 'Purple Passion' and mullein (*Verbascum bombyciferum*); *Cornus* 'Eddie's White Wonder'; TOP RIGHT: Perennial bed in early summer.

willow-like **mayten trees** (*Maytenus boaria*) with winter-blooming camellias growing in their shade.

Adjacent to the Garden of Perennials is the Moon-Viewing Garden, a shady Japanese-style garden with intimate and secluded surroundings.

3. Moon-Viewing Garden

Stepping stones to the right of the paved path beyond the Garden of Perennials lead to the cool, shady banks of a small stream. The rocks, the sound of the waterfall, and the varied green foliage of the shrubs and trees recall a mountain landscape. The Moon-Viewing Garden is designed for contemplation, strolling, and relaxation and seems far removed from the densely populated city.

The garden, designed in 1973, was a gift of the San Francisco Bay Area Chapter of Ikebana International. Typical of traditional Japanese gardens, color is used sparingly and serves to remind visitors of the changing seasons. **Azaleas** and **ornamental cherries** bloom in spring, and blue Japanese **irises** at the edge of the pond provide a splash of summer color. The golden yellows and reds of **Japanese**

maples usually reach their peak in November, and **magnolias** and **camellias** welcome in the first months of each new year.

Turn downstream, and the **moon-viewing deck** comes into view. The L-shaped wooden deck projects over the pond, where a nearby stream provides the relaxing sound of water. In the aristocratic Japanese tradition of moon-viewing gardens, a deck like this serves as a place for friends to celebrate the September full moon, composing poems and enjoying nature.

From the Moon-Viewing Garden, return to the Garden of Perennials, where the Collections Trail continues toward the Southeast Asian Cloud Forest.

OPPOSITE TOP: Flowering cherry (*Prunus* 'Okame'); THIS PAGE, TOP: Japanese maple (*Acer palmatum*); ABOVE RIGHT: Fall color maple leaves in stream; LEFT: *Camellia japonica* 'Anita'.

4. Southeast Asian Cloud Forest

The Southeast Asian Cloud Forest was set aside for plants from the mountains of Southeast Asia from the early days of the Garden, when it was known as Burma Road. In recent decades, it has featured **Vireya rhododendrons**, which thrive at cool and moist elevations between 7,000 and 12,000 feet on the moun-

tains of tropical Malaysia, Indonesia, the Philippines, and New Guinea, where temperatures are similar to those of San Francisco. Vireya rhododendrons are frost-sensitive and noted for their thick, fleshy, and often fragrant flowers in vivid shades of yellow, orange, and red. Some species are in bloom at any time of the year, with a peak in the spring. There are more than 300 known species of Vireyas, accounting for one-third of all rhododendron species. Plant explorers believe that many new species remain to be discovered in remote locations such as the rugged mountainous interior of New Guinea.

Fishtail palms are notable among the other plants. The common name comes from their triangular fishtail-like

TOP TO BOTTOM: Vireya rhododendron (*Rhododendron* 'George Bundsen'); Vireya rhododendron (*R.* 'Hundstein's Secret'); Vireya rhododendron (*R. konosi*); Vireya rhododendron (*R. laetum* x Lowii).

leaflets. The Himalayan fishtail palm (*Caryota urens*) is one of 12 species of *Caryota*, living in a region that extends from East Asia through the Malay Archipelago to northern Australia.

Cloud forest plants in the nursery. Bian Tan, plant collections manager between 1994 and 2002, collected seeds and cuttings from remote mountain locations and botanical gardens in Malaysia, Indonesia, Vietnam, and the Philippines. Many of these plants are currently being propagated in the nursery. The Garden also hosted colleagues from the Philippines and Indonesia who wished to study our procedures in plant identification, interpretation, education, and administration of botanical gardens. This arrangement serves the common goal of preserving rare and endangered plant species.

Current plans for the Southeast Asian Cloud Forest include a design by Linda Jewell, a landscape architect on the University of California, Berkeley faculty. The plan includes a small walk-through pavilion where orchids and insect-eating plants will be displayed. Since many of the new plants have not been cultivated previously, the gardeners look forward to experimenting with their care and maintenance. Repeat visitors will be able to share the excitement of watching this garden develop.

As you continue on the Collections Trail toward the Succulent Garden, the scenery shifts from a landscape of moisture-loving plants to one that features plants adapted to hot, dry climates.

5. Succulent Garden

Succulent plants survive long periods of drought by storing water in their leaves or stems. They take advantage of rare desert showers by soaking up enough water to tide them over a year or more of drought. The Succulent Garden is located in the warmest and driest place in the Garden. The sunny south-facing slope is terraced with stone walls, behind which sandy soil quickly drains off moisture. In this setting, many desert plants thrive outdoors, despite the cool, moist climate of coastal San Francisco.

Aloe saponaria.

The Succulent Garden was dedicated in 1971 in memory of the Garden's first director, Eric Walther. It emphasizes succulent plants native to the Western Hemisphere, where they are concentrated in semi-arid and arid regions of Mexico, the southwestern United States, and the western part of South America. South

Africa, in the Eastern Hemisphere, is home to different groups of succulents, some of which are also grown in the garden. Succulents are appreciated

for their varied patterns of growth, ranging from spiny stems to soft leafy rosettes in a variety of green and gray shades.

Leaf succulents. Most succulents in this garden store water in their leaves. These are called leaf succulents and belong to many different plant families.

Agave parryi variety **huachucensis** is native to Arizona; in the Succulent Garden, this leaf succulent grows against a south-facing limestone retaining wall, where the gray-green, spine-tipped leaves form a rosette. **Agave americana 'Medio Picta'** is a Mexican relative with striking bluish-green leaves that have contrasting pale yellow center stripes.

Puya chilensis produces a loose basal rosette of long, stiff, spiny leaves. In late winter, a huge asparagus-shaped flower stalk sprouts vertically

to a height of about 12 feet. In the spring, hundreds of buds open at the top of the stalk to reveal bright yellow flowers with orange male stamens. *Puya chilensis* is a native of Chile and is in the pineapple family. **Dyckia microcalyx** is a member of the same family as *Puya chilensis* and is native to Brazil.

Aloes are native to South Africa. **Tree aloes** (*Aloe arborescens*) bear abundant blossoms in winter that range in color from deep orange to red. **Aloe plicatilis** brightens the spring garden with orange flowers and distinctive banana-shaped leaves that are spread out like a fan. **Soap aloe** (*Aloe saponaria*) has rosettes of fleshy white-spotted leaves with branched stalks that produce orange-red flowers during the summer.

OPPOSITE, CLOCKWISE FROM TOP RIGHT: *Agave parryi* var. *huachucensis*; *Puya chilensis*; Succulent Garden: *Puya alpestris* to the right of steps and *Aeonium* species in the left foreground [SAXON HOLT]; Surrounded by succulents; THIS PAGE: *Agave parryi* var. *huachucensis* with *Aloe plicatilis* in the background [JOANNE TAYLOR].

Stem succulents. In contrast to leaf succulents, the cactus family stores water in its stems. Cactus species, which typically have spines instead of leaves, are almost all native to the Western Hemisphere.

Prickly pear (*Opuntia ficus-indica*) is a member of the cactus family that bears smooth, flat pads that are actually modified stems. The bright red fruits are the size and shape of a kiwi fruit, and after the spiny skin is peeled, the soft red-purple flesh is tasty and sweet. Prickly pear probably evolved in Mexico, where it is widely cultivated as a living fence. After being planted around the Mediterranean Sea and in Australia, it proved to be an invasive species.

Golden barrel cactus (*Echinocactus grussonii*) is a slow-growing rounded cactus with a dense armor of long pale yellow spines. It is native to Mexico.

After passing through the dry landscape of the Succulent Garden, the Collections Trail leads to the cool, moist, and shady surroundings of the Redwood Nature Trail. Follow one of the unpaved paths to the left and enter a grove of coast redwoods.

6. Redwood Nature Trail

The Redwood Nature Trail is the finest place to experience the serenity of a redwood forest without leaving the city. Over a century's worth of fallen leaf litter cushions the unpaved paths, and the benches in the subdued light are a pleasant place to relax and enjoy the cool, shady surroundings.

California's **coast redwoods** (*Sequoia sempervirens*) are not only the world's tallest trees, they are also among the fastest growing trees. Be sure to look up from the base of a trunk to appreciate the majestic height of these giants. In central and northern California, coast redwoods thrive in foggy, wind-protected coastal canyons that benefit from generous winter rain and streams that offer extra moisture to the roots. This garden provides the trees with similar conditions.

Coast redwoods have a shallow root system no more than a few feet deep, despite the great height of the trees. Each tree is supported by the wide spread of its roots, some of which are shallow enough to absorb surface moisture from fog drip during the summer. A thick, fibrous cushion of fire-resistant reddish-brown bark protects the massive trunks. At the base of some trunks, thin shoots with bright green foliage emerge from the burls. These shoots can grow into a new tree if the parent tree is destroyed by fire.

The redwood forest floor is carpeted with lush, green, shade-loving plants

Coast redwoods (*Sequoia sempervirens*).

with distinctive leaf patterns, including redwood sorrel, wild ginger, and western bleeding heart.

Redwood sorrel or **sour grass** (*Oxalis oregana*) forms a dense growth of dark green clover-shaped leaves. Both the leaves and stem are edible and have a sour taste that accounts for one of its common names. In late spring, pink flowers bloom at the end of short stalks.

Wild ginger (*Asarum caudatum*) produces shiny, heart-shaped leaves. In late spring, small maroon flowers emerge under the leaves. The plant is not related to true ginger but early settlers used it as a substitute in their cooking.

Western bleeding heart (*Dicentra formosa*) forms a carpet of finely divided fern-like leaves. From March to June, deep pink heart-shaped flowers hang from long naked stems, well above the foliage. Western bleeding heart is a shade-loving plant that requires rich, well-drained soil.

Skunk cabbage (*Lysichitum americanus*) favors boggy areas along the Redwood Nature Trail. Skunk cabbage has bright green oblong leaves that grow over two feet long. In mid-spring, yellow calla lily-like blossoms sprout and produce a skunk-like odor that attracts flies, which are their pollinators.

Red elderberry (*Sambucus racemosa*) is a tall shrub that contributes color to the forest in late spring.

TOP TO BOTTOM: Redwood sorrel (*Oxalis oregana*); Wild ginger (*Asarum caudatum*); Western bleeding heart (*Dicentra formosa*); Skunk cabbage (*Lysichitum americanus*); Red elderberry (*Sambucus racemosa*).

Return to the paved Collections Trail and walk to the next garden, which continues the theme of plants that are native to California.

7. California Garden

Once you reach the California Garden, follow one of the unpaved paths on your left to reach the stone circle, a comfortable place to rest and enjoy the view of an open California landscape. The garden was designed in 1986 by landscape architect Ron Lutsko Jr. Sections of this four-acre garden include chaparral, woodland, forest, a meadow, and a seasonally dry creek. Most of the plants are native to the coastal half of the state, where they grow under the influence of a mediterranean climate.

In **spring**, the meadow is known for its spectacular display of **wildflowers**.

California poppies (*Eschscholzia californica*) fill the meadow with bright orange blossoms that open during the middle hours of sunny days. In cloudy weather and at night, the petals fold to a closed position, protecting the pollen. The California poppy is California's state flower.

Meadow foam (*Limnanthes douglasii*) is an annual that forms large masses of flowers near the banks of the seasonal creek. The petals are yellow and fade to white at the outer edges. In California's Great Central Valley, meadow foam grows at the edges of vernal pools. Vernal pools are grassland depressions with poor drainage that collect water in winter and gradually dry up in spring.

Bush lupine (*Lupinus arboreus*) grows to a

TOP TO BOTTOM: Entrance to California garden; California poppies (*Eschscholzia californica*) and meadow foam (*Limnanthes douglasii*) [JOANNE TAYLOR]; Yellow bush lupine (*Lupinus arboreus*).

height of several feet and has distinctive leaves that are divided like the fingers of a hand. The yellow, lilac, or white clusters of flowers resemble sweet peas.

The flowers of **Western azalea** (*Rhododendron occidentale*) are so fragrant that they demand attention as you pass by. They bloom before the appearance of much foliage, with flower colors of white, pink, and peach.

Flannel bush (*Fremontodendron californicum*) is a small tree or shrub that grows in the chaparral of California's Coast Ranges and Sierra foothills. It bursts into bloom in late spring with fleshy gold-yellow blossoms.

Red buckwheat (*Eriogonum grande* variety *rubescens*) has clusters of small red flowers on stems that rise a foot above the foliage. One of the more vividly colored varieties of buckwheat, it is native to the Channel Islands of Southern California.

Farewell to spring (*Clarkia rubicunda*) displays deep pink flowers with four rounded petals that become darker toward their base. The flowers grow at the ends of thin red stems that are over a foot high.

TOP: Western azalea (*Rhododendron occidentale*); BOTTOM: Douglas iris (*Iris douglasii*) and Flannel bush (*Fremontodendron californicum*) [SAXON HOLT].

Sticky monkey flower (*Mimulus* 'Salsa') has a long late spring and summer blooming period. The leaves are dark and sticky, and the two-lipped flowers of this particular variety are colored bright red.

California buckeye (*Aesculus californica*) blooms in the late spring. A fine specimen of this tree with its rounded crown can be seen from the stone circle.

In **summer**, gumplant and Matilija poppy are in bloom:

Gumplant (*Grindelia stricta*) is a perennial that grows on the coastal bluffs of northern California and southern Oregon. The name gumplant refers to the shiny, white, glue-like substance that collects on the flower buds before they unfold to reveal yellow, daisy-like flowers.

Matilija poppy (*Romneya coulteri*) is a native of Southern California. The flower has large white crepe paper-like petals that surround a large center of bright yellow stamens, that suggest the image of the common name, "fried egg plant".

In **fall**, **California fuchsia** (*Epilobium canum*, formerly *Zauschneria californica)* produces brilliant orange-red, trumpet-shaped flowers that are pollinated by hummingbirds. The gray-green foliage provides an attractive background for the blossoms during the long blooming period.

In **winter**, **Manzanita** (*Arctostaphylos* sp.) shrubs bear small bell-shaped white or pink flowers. The shiny mahogany red bark is attractive all year round.

LEFT: Bark of *Arctostaphylos manzanita*; ABOVE, TOP TO BOTTOM: Sticky monkey flower (*Mimulus aurantiacus* 'Salsa'); Matilija poppy (*Romneya coulteri*); Manzanita (*Arctostaphylos hookeri* subsp. *franciscana*) [SAXON HOLT].

At the far end of the California Garden, return to the paved Collections Trail that leads you to East Asia Valley, the last garden on this walk.

8. East Asia Valley

East Asia Valley features plants from temperate and subtropical regions of East Asia, including southern China, Japan, and the eastern Himalayas. Most rhododendrons, camellias, and magnolias are native to these areas, and new species are still being discovered in remote places. This garden begins just beyond the California Garden, where a grove of dawn redwoods grows to the right of the paved path.

Dawn redwoods (*Metasequoia glyptostroboides*) were planted in this location during the late 1940s. They are relatives of California's coast redwood (*Sequoia sempervirens*) and giant sequoia (*Sequoiadendron giganteum*), but unlike those trees, they lose their needles each winter. Until 1941, botanists only knew dawn redwoods from fossil specimens. The discovery of a grove of living dawn redwoods

by a Chinese forester in a remote part of eastern Sichuan Province was an exciting event for botanists shortly after the Second World War.

In **winter** *and* **early spring,** ***Magnolia campbellii*** is among the first magnolias to bloom, with spectacular deep pink blossoms that are as large as ten inches across. The horizontally oriented outer petals and sepals encircle the vertical inner petals to form a cup-and-saucer shape.

Yulan magnolia (*Magnolia denudata*) has been grown in Chinese gardens since the Tang Dynasty (7th to 10th centuries).

Dawn redwood (*Metasequoia glyptostroboides*) [SAXON HOLT].

It was also the first East Asian magnolia introduced to the Western world when it was taken to England in 1780. Its lily-shaped blossoms are white and fragrant.

The genus **Michelia** is a member of the magnolia family that keeps its leaves during winter. In early spring, furry brown buds of **Michelia doltsopa** and **Michelia yunanensis** open to reveal delicate white blossoms.

Paperbush MITSU-MATA (*Edgeworthia chrysantha*) is a deciduous shrub native to China. It has long

TOP: *Magnolia sprengeri* [SAXON HOLT]; RIGHT, CLOCKWISE FROM TOP LEFT: *Magnolia soulangeana*; *Michelia doltsopa*; *Magnolia campbellii*; *Michelia yunanensis* [ALL BY SAXON HOLT].

been cultivated in Japan, where its stems are used to produce high-quality paper for banknotes. The yellow flowers, which emerge before the leaves, have a strong sweet fragrance.

In **late spring**, a **dove tree** (*Davidia involucrata*) near the dawn redwoods is covered by large, white, dove-like blossoms that display a pair of large, drooping modified leaves or bracts. The dove tree is native to mountains in southwestern China.

Tree peony (*Paeonia lutea*) is a shrub that grows in eastern Tibet. Unlike most peonies, this species does not require a period of severe winter chill to

bloom, and therefore it flowers well despite the mild winters in this garden.

LEFT: Blue bamboo (*Himalayacalamus hookerianus* [SAXON HOLT]; ABOVE, TOP TO BOTTOM: Dove tree (*Davidia involucrata*); Daylily (*Hemerocallis* 'Stella d'Oro'); Chinese tulip tree (*Liriodendron chinense*).

New canes of **blue bamboo** (*Himalayacalamus hookerianus*) that sprout in late spring have a striking bluish-purple color. This plant is native to the mid-elevations of the southern Himalayas, where it grows in the filtered light of the forest canopy. In California, it grows well in the mild climate along the coast.

In **summer**, **daylilies** such as *Hemerocallis* 'Stella d'Oro', with its gold-colored, trumpet-shaped blossoms, provide color for most of the season. Daylilies grow at forest edges and in meadows in China, Korea, and Japan.

In late **fall**, the unusual lobed leaves of the **Chinese tulip tree** (*Liriodendron chinense*) turn a bright yellow, and provide a welcome bit of fall color. This rare tree is native to a small and remote part of southwestern China.

In **winter**, **coral bark maple** (*Acer palmatum* 'Sango Kaku') has twigs and branches that turn a bright coral red after its leaves have fallen.

Coral bark maple (*Acer palmatum* 'Sango Kaku') [SAXON HOLT].

The Collections Trail ends at the Library Terrace.

The **Library Terrace** has several benches that afford visitors sweeping views of the Great Meadow. It is a good place to relax after having explored the Collections Trail. The Library Terrace is adjacent to the Library and the Bookstore.

Monastery Stones

The perimeter walls of the Library Terrace were built with carved limestone blocks from the remains of a 12th century Spanish monastery that was closed by the Spanish Government in 1835. Publisher William Randolph Hearst bought the neglected buildings in 1930 with approval of the government. They were then disassembled and shipped to California. The stones were never reassembled due to Hearst's financial setbacks during the Great Depression. In 1941, the city of San Francisco purchased the monastery stones from Hearst for the cost of storage. The crates were stored outdoors in Golden Gate Park, where fire and weather erased

most of the identifying marks, making future reconstruction impossible. Since the 1960s, the Garden has been able to incorporate the rectangular stones into retaining walls in many locations such as the Succulent, Fragrance, and California gardens. An opportunity for making creative use of arch stones and decorative column pieces was provided by the construction of the Terrace in 2000. The weathered monastery stones that enclose the Library Terrace give a long-established appearance to this recently built addition to the Garden.

Monastery stones on the library terrace.

THE ORIGIN OF GOLDEN GATE PARK AND THE GARDEN

San Francisco was a boomtown in the 1860s, following the 1849 Gold Rush and the construction of the first transcontinental railroad. With completion of the railroad in 1869, ambitious civic leaders envisioned a large park to rival New York City's newly successful Central Park, which featured plantings, rock formations, and ponds designed to suggest natural landscapes.

Political and economic pressures led to the selection of a 1,000-acre site in the undeveloped western half of San Francisco. Two-thirds of the land consisted of windswept, shifting sand dunes, and taming this wild setting proved to be a serious challenge. Frederick Law Olmsted, famous for his design of Central Park, warned against the choice of this location.

WILLIAM HAMMOND HALL MADE THE PARK A REALITY

The job of making a detailed site survey for the park was given to William Hammond Hall, an energetic and creative twenty-four-year-old Army-trained engineer. In 1870, he completed the survey within six months, during which he also prepared a preliminary design that included a site for a 12-acre botanical garden. Hall's organizational skills and research into park design led to his prompt appointment as Engineer of the Park. Over the next five years, he supervised the leveling and stabilization of the sand dunes. In the late 19th century, horses did most of the work that is now performed by gasoline-powered cars, trucks, and construction machinery. San Francisco had the costly job of disposing of the horse manure that littered its streets and stables. Hall was a recycling pioneer and transported the horse manure by light rail to the Park, where it was used as a soil amendment for new plantings.

William Hammond Hall as a young man.

Teams of horses drag heavy beams to level and contour the sand dunes.

Hall built a nursery in the eastern part of the Park, where it supplied the first 60,000 young trees. Tree plantings and curved roads were designed to provide protection from ocean winds, while yielding a natural and informal appearance. Among the most successful trees for this purpose were Monterey cypress (*Cupressus macrocarpa*) and Monterey pine (*Pinus radiata*), which are native to similarly wind-swept locations around the Monterey Peninsula, 100 miles south of San Francisco. A third introduced tree was the blue gum (*Eucalyptus globulus*) from southeastern Australia. The appearance of these three trees gives the landscape of Golden Gate Park and the Garden its distinctive character to this day.

Within five years, a location derided by critics was developing into a promising urban park, which gained strong public support. Even Olmsted was generous with his praise, writing: " I cannot too strongly express my admiration…There is no like enterprise anywhere else, which, so far as I can judge, has been conducted with equal foresight, ingenuity, and economy."

CONSERVATORY OF FLOWERS

The first indoor plant display in Golden Gate Park opened in 1879 with the completion of the Conservatory of Flowers, an exquisite, ornate, redwood and glass structure. The prefabricated pieces for the building had been purchased by real estate magnate James Lick for construction on his property in San Jose. When

Lick died in 1876, the materials for the Conservatory remained in unopened crates. A group of civic-minded donors then bought them from Lick's estate for assembly in Golden Gate Park.

For the next twelve decades, the Conservatory served as popular exhibition space for tropical plants that could not survive outdoors. In December 1995, windstorms severely damaged this historic landmark. Fortunately, a careful restoration was achieved with the help of generous donations. The reopening of the Conservatory in 2003, with innovative exhibits of tropical plants, was a resounding success with visitors of all ages. Large planting beds in front of the landmark building have changing seasonal displays of flowers that contribute to its appeal as one of San Francisco's favorite tourist attractions.

CALIFORNIA MIDWINTER INTERNATIONAL EXPOSITION OF 1894

San Francisco's Midwinter Fair of 1894 was the first world's fair held west of the Mississippi. Following on the heels of the 1893 World Columbian Exhibition in Chicago, the fair's January opening date served to advertise the city's mild winter climate. The fair attracted 2.5 million visitors and drew international attention to the year-round attractions of Golden Gate Park. The present Music Concourse, located between the De Young Museum and the California Academy of Sciences, was the center of the exhibit pavillions. The 266-foot-tall "Electric Light Tower," inspired by the Eiffel Tower previewed the latest in modern technology with a display of bright, blinking electric lights. The Japanese Tea Garden, the fair's most loved exhibit, was saved and remains equally popular with current visitors.

JOHN MCLAREN'S VISION FOR A WORLD-CLASS PARK

The development of Golden Gate Park into one of the world's great parks is due

John McLaren, Park Superintendent from 1887 to 1943.

Location for a
Future Botanical
Garden

Birdseye view of Golden Gate Park. The site of the future botanical garden is just to the left of Stow Lake and Strawberry Hill in the middle distance.

largely to the vision, skill, and long life span of John McLaren, who served as San Francisco's park superintendent from 1887 to 1943. Trained as a landscape gardener in Scotland, McLaren built up a worldwide network for collecting interesting plants and created the many informal landscapes for which the Park is known to this day.

McLaren chose the present site for a botanical garden, which is shown on an 1889 map of Golden Gate Park. The choice of this location, as described in his 1890 report to the Park Commission, was influenced by the presence of "a variety of soil and exposure, sloping, dry and sunny hillsides, sheltered spots and rich, low or marshy land." In 1898, a bond issue to establish an arboretum and botanical garden was placed on the San Francisco ballot, but narrowly failed to pass with the required two-thirds majority. But, the site was preserved, and trees were planted there with an eye toward the future. For example, a grove of coast redwoods was established sometime around 1900, accounting for mature and massive trees that grow along the present-day Redwood Nature Trail.

When McLaren was appointed landscape supervisor for the 1915 Panama Pacific International Exposition, he saw a special opportunity for acquiring a new group of rare trees. The fair that celebrated the opening of the Panama Canal was built on newly created landfill at a spectacular waterfront site that later became San Francisco's Marina District. New Zealand was represented by a landscaped exhibit building, and when the fair closed, McLaren welcomed a donation of the plants. Many of the donated trees have grown to maturity in the Garden.

The Origins of the Garden

Helene Strybing's Bequest Makes the Garden a Reality

The Garden finally became a reality after 1926 with the prospect of start-up funding. Helene Strybing, the prosperous widow of a San Francisco merchant, left a bequest of $200,000 to the city for the creation of an arboretum and botanical garden. The funds, a sizable fortune at the time, were gradually made available for use in the 1930s.

Construction Begins During the Great Depression

Eric Walther, the First Director

John McLaren hired Eric Walther as a gardener in 1918. Walther lacked a botanical background, but took the initiative of becoming a student of botanist Alice Eastwood at the California Academy of Sciences. McLaren was able to rely on Walther as his botanical expert by 1924 and gave him the responsibility for compiling the plant list included in the Golden Gate Park's annual report.

In 1937 Walther was placed in charge of the Garden and together he and

TOP: Helene Strybing provides startup funding for the Garden; BOTTOM: Eric Walther, Director of San Francisco Botanical Garden at Strybing Arboretum from 1937 to 1957, shown with *Magnolia campbellii*, his favorite tree.

McLaren developed the original plan. Construction and planting were carried out with the help of the Works Progress Administration (WPA), a federal program designed to provide jobs for unemployed workers during the Great Depression. Many of the Garden's first plants were raised in the Golden Gate Park nursery. In addition, nurseries and botanical gardens from around the world contributed seeds and plants.

The Garden Opened in 1940

When the Garden opened in 1940, it was designed around a central axis that still exists between the central fountain and the Garden of Perennials. Paths radiating from the central axis led to collections of plants from Australia, New Zealand, South Africa, the Mediterranean Basin, China, the Himalayas, Japan, Mexico, Central and South America, and California. The arrangement of plants according to their land of origin was a relatively new concept for gardens in North America. Botanical gardens of that time typically grouped related plants, such as maples or oaks, and displayed colorful perennial borders and beds of annuals.

Walther was an enthusiast of deciduous magnolias native to East Asia, and the Garden soon became internationally renowned for its collection. His success in cultivating *Magnolia campbellii* was well publicized. This species only comes into bloom after an unusually long 20-year or so delay. When a specimen in the Gardens flowered late in the winter of 1940, it was the first such occurrence in the Western Hemisphere and attracted enormous crowds.

Eric Walther remained the Director of the Garden until his retirement in 1957. During his tenure, he emphasized public education, implementing guided tours and arranging displays of ornamental plants that could be grown successfully in the San Francisco area.

San Francisco Botanical Garden Society

As Walther's retirement approached, his friends formed what was called the Strybing Arboretum Society in 1955 to help support the Garden and maintain its educational programs. The non-profit Society has helped fund the design and planting of several collections over the years. In 1972, it supported the construction and maintenance of the Helen Crocker Russell Library of Horticulture. Today, as the San Francisco Botanical Garden Society, the organization also raises funds for new projects and for the renovation of existing sections of the Garden. It operates the library, bookstore, and plant sales and offers a wide range of classes, tours, and workshops for children and adults.

Robert Tetlow's Master Plan of 1959

Plans were approved in 1958 for the construction of a large auditorium and exhibition hall. The Recreation and Park Commission hired Robert Tetlow, a professor of landscape architecture at the University of California, Berkeley, to integrate this building with the Garden as a whole and to prepare a comprehensive long-range master plan.

Tetlow's plan included many of the Garden's prominent features, in particular the Main Gate with its expansive view across the Great Meadow to the central fountain. Later, in 1986, Tetlow designed the Friend Gate, across the road from the Japanese Tea Garden, to be the northern entrance to the Garden.

Later Developments

During the 1970s, the Moon-Viewing Garden was designed and the California Garden was expanded. In the 1980s and 1990s, Director Walden Valen revised the plant collections plan to take better advantage of San Francisco's mild coastal climate. Collections from mediterranean and other mild temperate climate regions were expanded, and less emphasis was given to plants from colder northern regions of Asia, Europe, and North America. New gardens were created, such as the South Africa Garden, and major renovations were made to the California, Australia, and Chile and South America gardens. In addition, a large area was set aside for plants collected from tropical cloud forests of Central America by Dr. Dennis Breedlove, a botanist on the staff of the California Academy of Sciences. A garden of plants from the cloud forests of Southeast Asia, including tropical Vireya rhododendrons, was also established. The cloud forest collections are a unique feature of the Garden today.

A 1995 update of the master plan, by landscape architects Tito Patri Associates and architects Fernau & Hartman focused on a new nursery, a visitor center, and the expansion of the library. New gardens representing lands around the Mediterranean Sea and cloud forests of Southeast Asia were projected. Also included were improvements to the entrances.

Robert Tetlow with his plan for the Gardens.

The 1995 master plan was further refined in 2001 by the Portico Group, a Seattle-based firm specializing in botanical garden design. Three major loop trails were planned for the pedestrian pathways, which form the basis for the three walks covered in this guide.

Anticipating the Future

Scot Medbury, director of the Garden, and the San Francisco Botanical Garden Society under the leadership of Michael McKechnie have developed ambitious plans for the next few years. Through a capital campaign sponsored by the Society, our goal for the future is to transform San Francisco's Garden into one of the world's finest.

Garden improvement projects include the renovation of seven gardens representing plant collections from around the world. A new garden, the Southeast Asian Cloud Forest will take advantage of San Francisco's mild climate and will be the first of its kind anywhere. A position for an additional gardener will assure improved maintenance of the whole Garden.

A *Center for Sustainable Gardening* is planned to assure modern and efficient facilities to propagate plants for the entire Garden, for hands on learning by adults and children, and for hosting plant sales, an important source of income for the Society. The structure will be an environmentally sensitive "green" building that will demonstrate a positive impact on its environment.

Accessible paths and a well-designed wayfinding system will make the Garden more welcoming. Regrading and repaving of paths will improve access for those with limited mobility, and a color-coded wayfinding system will help visitors to enjoy the three self-guided walks described in this Guide.

The Garden improvement projects, the *Center for Sustainable Gardening*, and the wayfinding system will combine to enhance the Society's vibrant and growing community education programs. We see the Botanical Garden becoming the "trailhead" for Bay Area residents and visitors to become increasingly engaged in the natural world and to serve as good stewards of our natural environment.

Coast redwoods (*Sequoiadendron sempervirons*) [SAXON HOLT].